MW00622743

THIEVES® QUICK VIEW

THIEVES® ESSENTIAL OIL BLEND

1. Boost Shampoo. Add 5 drops per ounce to your favorite shampoo to boost its cleansing power.

2. Boost Hand Purifier. Add 5 drops per ounce to your favorite hand purifier to scent it and boost it's purifying power.

3. Respiratory System Support. Combine 1 drop Thieves Essential Oil Blend with 1 drop carrier oil.. Apply directly to the skin of your upper chest and throat for respiratory system support.

4. Support Healing. Combine 1 drop of Thieves Essential Oil Blend with 1 drop of carrier oil. Apply to light abrasions to help prevent infection and promote healing.

5. Support Healing. Combine 1 drop of Thieves Essential Oil Blend with 1 drop of carrier oil. Apply to bandages before placing over wounds to help prevent infection.

6. Blemishes. Combine 12 drops of Thieves Essential Oil Blend with ½ teaspoon of aloe vera gel and apply to blemishes.

7. Cold Recovery. Diffuse 30 drops of Thieves Essential Oil Blend in a 100ml water-based diffuser in a room to support recovery from a cold.

8. Energy & Immunity. Diffuse 20 drops of Thieves Essential Oil Blend in a water-based USB diffuser or personal diffuser to support energy and immunity.

9. Purify Air. Diffuse 20 drops of Thieves Essential Oil Blend in a water-based car diffuser to purify the air and counter pollution.

10. Support Clear Sinuses. Diffuse 30 drops of Thieves Essential Oil Blend in a personal diffuser to help clear the sinuses and support respiratory health.

11. Support Healthy Lungs. Diffuse 30 drops of Thieves Essential Oil Blend in a personal diffuser to help clear the lungs and support respiratory wellness.

12. Energize the Body. Inhale Thieves Essential Oil Blend directly from bottle to energize the body.

13. Sinus Health Support. Put 2 of Thieves Essential Oil Blend drops in palm. Rub palms together. Cup hands & inhale for sinus health support.

14. Support Ear Health 1. Apply 2 drops of Thieves Essential Oil Blend and 2 drops of carrier oil to a cotton ball. Massage around the outside of the ears.

15. Support Ear Health 2. Apply 2 drops of Thieves Essential Oil Blend and 2 drops of carrier oil to a cotton ball. Massage behind the ears.

16. Support Lymphatic System 1. Add 30 drops of Thieves Essential Oil Blend to a 5 ml or 1 dram vial with dropper. Add 30 drops of carrier. Mix thoroughly. Apply 2 drops to the lymph nodes on the neck.

17. Support Lymphatic System 2. Add 30 drops of Thieves Essential Oil Blend to a 5 ml or 1 dram vial with dropper. Add 30 drops of carrier. Mix thoroughly. Apply 2 drops to the lymph nodes under the arms.

18. Support Heart Health 1. Locating the reflexology point located in the palm of your left hand—between the ring finger and the little finger, just inside the base of the little finger bone—apply 2 drops of Thieves Essential Oil Blend and press this point using your thumb. Apply pressure from 30 seconds up to a minute. Do this two or three times a day.

19. Support Heart Health 2. Locating the heart meridian on the round bone at the base of your palm, tracing toward the inside bottom border of the bone (the Shen Men or Spirit Gate in Chinese Acupuncture) apply 2 drops of Thieves Essential Oil Blend. Press inward, using a circular motion for 30 seconds to a minute. Do this two or three times a day.

20. Support Heart Health 3. Place the tip of your thumb just below the throat pit. Let the remaining fingers naturally touch the area on the chest, towards the point where the shoulder meets the left arm. Add 2 drops of Thieves Essential Oil Blend. Use the pads of your fingers to lightly press up and down 5 times every day.

21. Travel 1. Put 10 drops of Thieves Essential Oil Blend in a 5 ml roller bottle. Fill with carrier oil. Roll a strip under your nose (above your upper lip) when you go on a plane.

22. Travel 2. Put 10 drops of Thieves Essential Oil Blend in a 5 ml roller bottle. Fill with carrier oil. Swipe a roll under your nose (above your upper lip) when you take the bus.

23. Travel 3. Put 10 drops of Thieves Essential Oil Blend in a 5 ml roller bottle. Fill with carrier oil. Swipe a roll under your nose (above your upper lip) when you take the bus.

24. Travel 4. Put 10 drops of Thieves Essential Oil Blend in a 5 ml roller bottle. Fill with carrier oil. Swipe a roll under your nose (above your upper lip) when you are going to common areas of a cruise.

25. Purify Hotel Room. Diffuse 20 drops of Thieves Essential Oil Blend in a water-based single room diffuser when in your hotel room to purify the air and counter pollution.

26. Clothes Freshening Spray. Add 20 drops of Thieves Essential Oil Blend to a 1-ounce amber glass spray bottle. Fill with neutral rectified spirits. Shake well. Use as a spray to freshen clothes and kill germs.

27. Spray Purifier for Clothes. Add 20 drops of Thieves Essential Oil Blend to a 1-ounce amber glass spray bottle. Fill with neutral rectified spirits. Shake well. Use as a spray to areas of clothes that come in contact with potentially dirty seats, germs, etc.

28. Room Clarifier Spray. Add 20 drops of Thieves Essential Oil Blend to a 1-ounce amber glass spray bottle. Fill with neutral rectified spirits. Shake well. Spray room to clarify the air.

29. Bathroom Freshening Spray. Add 20 drops of Thieves Essential Oil Blend to a 1-ounce amber glass spray bottle. Fill with neutral rectified spirits. Shake well. Use as a spray to freshen the bathroom.

30. Toilet Freshening Spray. Add 20 drops of Thieves Essential Oil Blend to a 1-ounce amber glass spray bottle. Fill with neutral rectified spirits. Shake well. Spray the bowl 5x before each use to freshen the toilet.

31. Kitchen Spray. Add 20 drops of Thieves Essential Oil Blend to a 1-ounce amber glass spray bottle. Fill with neutral rectified spirits. Shake well. Use as a spray to freshen the kitchen after cooking.

32. House Freshening. Add 40 drops of Thieves Essential Oil Blend to a 1-ounce amber glass spray bottle. Fill with neutral rectified spirits. Shake well. Use as a spray to freshen the whole house and cleanse the air.

33. Purify Pet Cages. Add 40 drops of Thieves Essential Oil Blend to a 1-ounce amber glass spray bottle. Fill with neutral rectified spirits. Shake well. Use to spray and wipe down pet cages to create a healthy environment.

34. Vita-Flex Roller Protection: Adults. Add 50 drops of Thieves Essential Oil Blend to a 10 ml amber glass roller bottle. Fill with carrier oil. Shake well. Roll on Vita-Flex points on feet for immune support.

35. Vita-Flex Roller Protection: Kids. Add 40 drops of Thieves Essential Oil Blend to a 10 ml amber glass roller bottle. Fill with carrier oil. Shake well. Roll on children's feet for immune support before they leave the house.

36. Vita-Flex Roller Protection: Dogs. Add 20 drops of Thieves Essential Oil Blend to a 10 ml amber glass roller bottle. Fill with carrier oil. Shake well. Roll on Vita-Flex points on dog's paws for immune support.

37. Purify Office. Diffuse 20 drops of Thieves Essential Oil Blend in a water-based single room diffuser when in your office to purify the air and counter pollution.

38. Dishwasher Boost. Add 10 drops of Thieves Essential Oil Blend to your dishwasher detergent when you fill the dispenser for cleaner dishes.

39. Laundry Boost. Add 10 drops of Thieves Essential Oil Blend to your laundry cycle for cleaner clothes.

40. Mopping Boost. Add 15 drops of Thieves Essential Oil Blend to your mop water for cleaner floors.

41. Protect Houseplants. Mix 30 drops of Thieves Essential Oil Blend with 2 ounces of water in an amber glass spray bottle. Shake well. Mist over houseplants to help repel insects.

42. De-Gum Adhesive. Combine 5 drops of Thieves Essential Oil Blend with 10 drops of carrier. Apply with a dropper and dissolve the gummy adhesive on price labels/stickers.

43. Bee Sting. Remove stinger. Mix 1 teaspoon baking soda with 10 drops of water and 10 drops of Thieves Essential Oil Blend. Apply to sting area to help neutralize.

44. Wasp Sting. Mix 10 drops of Thieves Essential Oil Blend with ½ teaspoon of vinegar. Using a cotton swab, dab the area repeatedly (gently) to help neutralize.

45. Mosquito Bite. Combine 30 drops of Thieves Essential Oil Blend with 30 drops of carrier in a 1 dram or 5 ml amber/cobalt glass vial with dropper. Mix well. Place 1-4 drops of the mixture on bug bites 3-5 times a day.

46. Ant Deterrent. Combine 30 drops of Thieves Essential Oil Blend with 2 ounces of distilled water. Spray in the area that ants track, including their nest.

47. Spider Deterrent. Combine 40 drops of Thieves Essential Oil Blend with 2 ounces of distilled water. Spray around window sills, door jambs, corners, and areas where you generally see spiders.

48. Fresh Feet. Apply 3 drops of Thieves Essential Oil Blend directly to the bottoms of feet. Massage into feet to start your day.

49. Fungal Deterrent. Apply up to 4 drops of Thieves Essential Oil Blend directly to areas on each foot (paying particular attention to the toes) to combat fungus.

50. Make a Foot Roller. Add 50 drops of Thieves Essential Oil Blend to a 5ml amber glass steel ball roller. Fill with carrier oil. Roll daily on the bottoms of feet to support wellness.

51. Natural Cleaning Scrub. Mix 50 drops of Thieves Essential Oil Blend with 4 tablespoons baking soda and 1 tablespoon of water to create a natural cleaning scrub good for tile, grout, toilets, bathtubs, showers, and sinks.

52. Clean Sticky Paws. Dilute Thieves Essential Oil Blend 1 drop to 2 drops carrier oil. Apply with a cotton ball to the bottoms of sticky dog or cat paws. Finish by removing excess with a paper towel.

53. Healthy Dog/Cat Teeth. Dilute Thieves Essential Oil Blend 1 drop to 2 drops carrier oil. Apply with a cotton swab to where the teeth meet the gum line on your dog or cat to support oral health.

54. Freshen Spa. Add a few drops of Thieves Essential Oil Blend weekly to your hot tub or spa to create a more invigorating aroma.

55. Invigorating Lotion. Add 5 drops of Thieves Essential Oil Blend per ounce of your favorite lotion. Massage on muscles and joints after working out.

THIEVES® VITALITY™ ESSENTIAL OIL DIETARY SUPPLEMENT

Aromatic · Topical · Dietary

56. Healthy Throat. Mix 2 drops of Thieves® Vitality™ with a tablespoon of water, gargle & swallow to support a healthy throat.

57. Immunity. Put 8-10 drops of Thieves® Vitality™ in a vegetable gelatin capsule undiluted and swallow daily to support a healthy immune system.

58. Longevity. Put 8-10 drops of Thieves® Vitality™ in a vegetable gelatin capsule undiluted and swallow daily to support longevity.

59. Clear Skin. Put 8-10 drops of Thieves® Vitality™ in a vegetable gelatin capsule undiluted and swallow daily to support healthy, clear skin.

60. Stress Head. Put a drop of Thieves® Vitality™ on a cotton swab with a drop of carrier. Apply to the roof of your mouth. Push with your tongue and let the stress dissipate.

61. Support Healthy Gums. Dip a fresh piece of floss in 1 drop of Thieves Vitality and 1 drop of carrier. Floss as usual to support healthy gums.

62. Support Reduced Plaque. Using a cotton swab, apply 1 drop of Thieves Vitality with 1 drop of carrier to areas near the gums where the teeth come together. This will help keep plaque from building up in those problem areas.

63. Healthy Teeth & Gums. Using a cotton swab, apply 1 drop of Thieves Vitality with 1 drop of carrier to gums and teeth to support dental health.

64. Health Support. Put 1 drop of Thieves Vitality in your cup of tea for flavor and to maintain health.

65. Smoking Cessation. Put 1 drop of Thieves Vitality with 1 drop of carrier on the tip of your tongue to help stave off smoking cravings. Add a drop of Clove and carrier for added effect.

66. Cold Sores. Using a cotton swab, apply 1 drop of Thieves Vitality with 1 drop of carrier to cold sores to help support healing.

67. Cankers. Using a cotton swab, apply 1 drop of Thieves Vitality with 1 drop of carrier to canker sores to help support healing.

68. Bitten Cheek. Using a cotton swab, apply 1 drop of Thieves Vitality with 1 drop of carrier to areas where you may bite your cheek to help support healing.

69. Orthodontic sores. Using a cotton swab, apply 1 drop of Thieves Vitality with 1 drop of carrier to areas where braces or retainers cause mouth cuts to help support healing.

70. Scratchy Throat. Put 1 drop of Thieves Vitality in your orange juice and drink to help cut phlegm and congestion.

71. Ward Off the Ick. Put 3 drops of Thieves Vitality in water or juice every three hours at the first sign of a cold.

72. Breakouts. Place a drop of Thieves Vitality with 1 drop of carrier on the tongue and a drop in a glass of water every day to help support fewer breakouts.

73. Soothe Swallowing. Mix 3 drops of Thieves Vitality with a teaspoon of honey and a teaspoon of lemon juice to soothe a cough.

74. Vocal Tonic. Place a drop of Thieves Vitality with 1 drop of carrier under tongue to restore voice.

75. Support Immune System Internally. Place 10 drops of Thieves Vitality in a vegan gelatin capsule every day when exposed to people who have been sick.

THIEVES® AUTOMATIC DISHWASHER POWDER

Aromatic · Cleansing

76. Replace Your Current Dishwasher Powder. Use Thieves Automatic Dishwasher Powder in place of your current dishwashing detergent.

77. Make a Heavy Degreaser. Combine 1 tablespoon of Thieves Automatic Dishwasher Powder with 1 cup of distilled water.

78. Make a Carpet/Upholstery Spot Cleaner. Mix 1 tablespoon of Thieves Automatic Dishwasher Powder with 6 cups of water. Combine thoroughly.

THIEVES® DISH SOAP

79. Hand Cleaning. Wash hands thoroughly with warm water.

80. Washing Dishes By Hand. Use as directed to wash dishes by hand.

81. DIY: Foamer. Add 2 Tablespoons of Thieves Dish Soap to your empty foamer. Fill with distilled water. Shake well to mix. Use as your regular Thieves Foaming Hand Soap.

82. Car Wash Solution: Add 2 tablespoons of Thieves Dish Soap to 2 gallons of water. Using a gentle sponge, massage soapy mixture into dirty areas of your car. Rinse thoroughly.

83. Leather Protection: Mix 6 drops of Thieves Dish Soap with 2 cups of distilled water and ½ cup of olive oil in an amber glass spray bottle. Shake well. Spray leather and wipe away excess with a rag or paper towel.

84. Dusting. Add 5 drops of Thieves Dish Soap to a soft, damp cloth or rag. Dust tables, tchotchkes, and décor.

85. Plant Shine. Add 5 drops of Thieves Dish Soap to an amber glass spray bottle. Fill with distilled water. Shake well. Spray down plants and gently wipe clean.

86. Jewelry Cleaner: Add a drop of Thieves Dish Soap to your jewelry. Massage with a soft rag or toothbrush. Rinse thoroughly for a beautiful shine.

87. Fingernail Scrub. Add a drop of Thieves Dish Soap to a fingernail brush and gently massage cuticles and under dirty fingernails for healthy clean nails.

88. Toenail Scrub. Add a drop of Thieves Dish Soap to a nail brush and gently massage cuticles and under dirty toenails for healthy clean nails.

89. Upholstery Spot Cleaner. (Spot test before using.) Add 1-2 drops to the spot. Massage with a damp rag. Use a clean, dry rag to dab out the spot.

90. Carpet Spot Cleaner. (Spot test before using.) Add 1-2 drops to the spot. Massage with a damp rag. Use a clean, dry rag to dab out the spot.

91. Clothing Spot Cleaner. (Spot test before using.) Add 1-2 drops to the spot. Massage with a damp rag. Use a dry towel (or paper towel) to dab out the spot.

92. Automatic Dishwasher Detergent. In a pinch, try adding 7 drops and a tablespoon of baking soda to the powder dispenser.

93. Shampoo Substitute. Use in place of shampoo and add your favorite essential oils.

94. Body Wash Substitute. Use as a body wash substitute for a healthy, clean, fresh smelling shower.

95. Sink Cleaning. Use a dollop and a scrub brush to clean stains away from the sink.

96. Tub Cleaning. Add 2 squirts to the tub. Sprinkle in baking soda. Scrub the mixture around the tub. Rinse thoroughly.

97. Clean Whirlpool Bath. Add 2 squirts to the tub. Fill with water. Run whirlpool jets for 10 minutes. Drain the tub. Rinse thoroughly.

98. De-Gum Adhesive. Apply directly to the gummy adhesive on price labels/stickers.

99. Polishing Wood Soap: Mix 2 tablespoons of Thieves Dish Soap with 1 cup of distilled water and ¼ cup of olive oil in an amber glass spray bottle. Shake well. Spray and wipe cabinets, banisters, and wooden servingware.

THIEVES®
FRUIT & VEGGIE SOAK
Aromatic · Cleansing

100. Clean Germs & Pesticide Residue. Use as directed to clean produce.

THIEVES®
FRUIT & VEGGIE SPRAY
Aromatic · Cleansing

101. Portably Clean Germs & Pesticide Residue.
Use portably as directed to clean produce.

THIEVES® HOUSEHOLD CLEANER

Aromatic · Cleansing

102. Create Your Own Wipes.
Cut a roll of strong paper towels in half. In a glass pitcher or pourable mixing bowl, combine one capful of Thieves Household Cleaner with 1½ cups of distilled water and 5 drops of Thieves essential oil. Place the half paper towel roll in a glass jar. Pour mixture over. Seal the jar. Roll the jar until the towels are evenly saturated. Use as wipes.

103. Refill Foamer Pump Bottle. Combine ½ cup of Thieves Household Cleaner with ½ cup of water. Fill your empty foamer bottle. Use as normal.

104. Use in Dishwasher. Use 1 capful of Thieves Household cleaner in place of your automatic dishwasher detergent.

105. Use in Clothes Washer 1. Mix 1 capful of Thieves Household Cleaner in 1 cup water, add to water for the wash cycle.

106. Use in Clothes Washer 2. Add 1-2 capfuls of Thieves Household Cleaner to the detergent bin at start of wash.

107. Use to Hand-Wash Fabrics. Fill sink halfway with water. Add 2 capfuls to the water. Swish gently. Soak clothes. Gently squeeze and swish. Allow to sit for 30 minutes. Rinse.

108. Use as Fabric Softener. Pour ½ capful of Thieves Household Cleaner on a face cloth to soak. Put it in the dryer instead of a dryer sheet.

109. Make an All-Purpose Cleaner. Mix 1 capful of Thieves Household Cleaner with 2-3 cups of distilled water. Store in 2-3 8-ounce amber glass spray bottles.

110. All-Purpose for Bathroom Sink. Using the all-purpose cleaner spray recipe above and soft, lint-free rag, spray and wipe away germs, scum, mineral, and stains from the bathroom sink.

111. All-Purpose for Toilet Bowl. Using the all-purpose cleaner spray recipe above, spray the inside of the bowl. Wait 2 minutes. Spray again. Use a toilet bowl brush to scrub away stains. Flush. Repeat.

112. All-Purpose for Bathroom Floor 1. Using the all-purpose cleaner spray recipe above, spray the bathroom floor. With a clean towel, wipe gently.

113. All-Purpose for Bathroom Floor 2. Using the all-purpose cleaner spray recipe above, spray the bathroom floor. Mop dry with clean, soft mop.

114. All-Purpose for Baseboards. Using the all-purpose cleaner spray recipe above, spray the baseboards. Wipe gently clean.

115. All-Purpose for Window Sills. Using the all-purpose cleaner spray recipe above, spray the window sills. Wipe gently clean.

116. All-Purpose for Blinds. Using the all-purpose cleaner spray recipe above, spray the blinds. Wipe gently clean.

117. All-Purpose for Shower. Using the all-purpose cleaner spray recipe above, spray the inside of the shower. Wait 2 minutes. Spray again. Pay close attention to stained, soap-scum-ridden areas, or moldy spots. Rinse clean.

118. All-Purpose for Bathtub. Using the all-purpose cleaner spray recipe above, spray the inside of the bathtub thoroughly. Wait 2 minutes. Spray again. Pay close attention to stained, soap-scum-ridden areas, or moldy spots. Rinse clean.

119. All-Purpose for Kitchen Sink. Using the all-purpose cleaner spray recipe above, spray the inside of the kitchen sink. Wait 2 minutes. Spray again. Pay close attention to stained, soap-scum-ridden areas, or moldy spots. Rinse clean.

120. All-Purpose for Counter Tops. Using the all-purpose cleaner spray recipe above, spray the countertops as normal. Wipe clean and dry with a soft rag.

121. All-Purpose for Stovetops. Using the all-purpose cleaner spray recipe above, spray the stovetop as normal. Wipe clean and dry with a soft rag.

122. All-Purpose for Floors 1. Using the all-purpose cleaner spray recipe above, spray the floors, and wipe clean and dry with a soft rag.

123. All-Purpose for Floors 2. Using the all-purpose cleaner spray recipe above, place in "Swiffer" or similar mop reservoir. Spray and wipe as normal.

124. All-Purpose for Floors 3. Using the all-purpose cleaner spray recipe above, drench a soft, clean towel with the solution. Walk gently across the floors to clean up dust and give the floors a marvelous shine.

125. All-Purpose for Floors 4. Using the all-purpose cleaner spray recipe above, fill a small bucket and mop with a classic, braided cotton-headed mop.

126. All-Purpose for Chrome Fixtures. Using the all-purpose cleaner spray recipe above, spray the fixtures, and wipe clean and dry with a soft, lint-free rag.

127. All-Purpose for Doors. Using the all-purpose cleaner spray recipe above, spray the areas of doors where greasy hands tend to touch and leave marks. Pay close attention to where feet also scuff bottoms. Wipe clean with a soft cloth.

128. All-Purpose for Cleaning Tools. Using the all-purpose cleaner spray recipe above, soak sponges, rags, and mop heads to clean and disinfect.

129. All-Purpose for Travel 1. Using the all-purpose cleaner spray recipe above, spray your seat and headrest of a bus, train, or airplane.

130. All-Purpose for Travel 2. Using the all-purpose cleaner spray recipe above, spray buttons, trays, and armrests of your travel seat.

131. Make a Heavy Degreaser. Combine 1 capful Thieves Household Cleaner with 1 cup of distilled water.

132. Clean Oven Racks. Using heavy degreaser recipe above and a sponge, wipe down the oven racks. Then, using a natural scrubbing brush or sponge, gently massage away grime and burned-on grease. Rinse. Repeat.

133. Clean Microwave Oven. Steam ½ cup of water in microwave for 1 minute. Using heavy degreaser recipe above and a sponge, wipe down the inside of the microwave oven.

134. Clean Oven. Using the heavy degreaser recipe above and a sponge, wipe down the inside of the oven. Using a painter's razor blade, gently scrape areas with burned, caked-one grease. Wipe again with degreaser solution and steel wool or scouring pad. Rinse. Repeat.

135. Clean Outdoor Grill. Scrape excess ash with a brass brush or steel wool. Using the heavy degreaser recipe above and a scouring pad, clean the racks. Rinse. Repeat.

136. Clean Greasy Stainless Pan. Add ½ cup of heavy degreaser to pan. Heat on stove until simmering (smells great, too). Move to sink. Allow to safely cool until tolerable. Using a gentle scouring pad, massage the grease away. Rinse. Repeat.

137. Clean Refrigerator. Using heavy degreaser recipe above and a sponge, wipe down the inside of the refrigerator, including racks, shelves, and doors.

138. Clean Car White Walls. Using ¼ cup of heavy degreaser recipe, add 1 tablespoon of baking soda. With a toothbrush, gently scrub the white walls until clean.

139. Clean Dutch Oven. Add ½ cup of heavy degreaser to Dutch oven. Soak overnight. Using a gentle scouring pad, massage the grease away. Rinse. Repeat.

140. Make a Glass Cleaner. Mix 1 capful of Thieves Household Cleaner, 5 drops of Citrus Fresh™ essential oil blend, and 1 teaspoon of white vinegar with 3 cups of distilled water.

141. Streak-Free Mirrors. Using the glass cleaner recipe above, spray liberally and wipe clean with a lint-free cloth.

142. Clean Car Windows. Using the glass cleaner recipe above, spray liberally and wipe clean with a lint-free cloth.

143. Clean Car Mirrors. Using the glass cleaner recipe above, spray liberally and wipe clean with a lint-free cloth.

144. Make a Deep Cleaning Scrub. Mix equal parts Thieves Household Cleaner and baking soda to form a thick paste.

145. Deep Clean Toilet. Using the deep cleaning scrub recipe above, apply mixture with clean cloth, sponge, or toilet brush. Scrub surface gently but thoroughly. Rinse clean. Repeat.

146. Deep Clean Bathtub. Using the deep cleaning scrub recipe above, apply mixture with clean cloth, sponge, or brush. Scrub surface gently but thoroughly. Rinse clean. Repeat.

147. Deep Clean Shower. Using the deep cleaning scrub recipe above, apply mixture with clean cloth, sponge, or brush. Scrub surface gently but thoroughly. Rinse clean. Repeat.

148. Deep Clean Kitchen Sink. Using the deep cleaning scrub recipe above, apply mixture with clean cloth, sponge, or brush. Scrub surface gently but thoroughly. Rinse clean. Repeat.

149. Deep Clean Tile Grout. Using the deep cleaning scrub recipe above, apply mixture with clean cloth, sponge, or brush. Scrub surface gently but thoroughly. Rinse clean. Repeat.

150. Deep Clean Glass-Top Stove. Using the deep cleaning scrub recipe above, apply mixture with clean cloth, sponge, or brush. Scrub surface gently but thoroughly. Rinse clean. Repeat.

151. Make a Carpet/Upholstery Spot Cleaner. Mix 1 capful of Thieves Household Cleaner with 6 cups of water. Combine thoroughly.

152. Spot Clean Carpets. Using an 8-ounce amber glass bottle, filled with the above spot-cleaning recipe, apply to spotted areas of carpet or rugs. Dab (don't rub) the area gently and use a rag to draw up the stain.

153. Spot Clean Sofas. Using an 8-ounce amber glass bottle filled with the above spot-cleaning recipe, apply to spotted areas of upholstery on sofas, loveseats, and chairs. Dab (don't rub) the area gently and use a rag to draw up the stain.

154. Spot Clean Laundry. Using an 8-ounce amber glass bottle filled with the above spot-cleaning recipe, apply to laundry spots. Dab (don't rub) the area gently and use a rag to draw up the stain. Wash as usual.

155. Spot Clean Car Seats. Using an 8-ounce amber glass bottle filled with the above spot-cleaning recipe, apply to spotted areas of your car seats. Dab (don't rub) the area gently and use a rag to draw up the stain.

156. Spot Clean Car Carpets. Using an 8-ounce amber glass bottle filled with the above spot-cleaning recipe, apply to spotted areas of your car seats. Dab (don't rub) the area gently and use a rag to draw up the stain.

157. Remove Gum. Using an 8-ounce amber glass bottle filled with the above spot-cleaning recipe, apply to areas that have gum. Gently massage the area to work the gum free.

158. Remove Tar. Using an 8-ounce amber glass bottle filled with the above spot-cleaning recipe, apply to areas that have tar. Gently massage the area to work the tar free.

159. Remove Sticker Residue. Using an 8-ounce amber glass bottle filled with the above spot-cleaning recipe, apply to areas that have sticker residue. Gently massage the area to work the sticky residue free.

160. Remove Pine Pitch From Outdoor Furniture. Using an 8-ounce amber glass bottle filled with the above spot-cleaning recipe, apply to spotted areas of outdoor cushions or upholstery on sofas, loveseats, and chairs. Dab (don't rub) the area gently and use a rag to draw up the stain.

161. Remove Stains on Concrete Grill Pad. Spray the concrete thoroughly. Let sit for 15 minutes. Gently scrub with a brush. Hose down or wipe clean.

162. Remove Stains on Patios. Spray the patio area thoroughly. Let sit for 15 minutes. Gently scrub stained areas with a brush. Hose down or wipe clean.

163. Remove Stains on Sidewalks. Spray the concrete thoroughly. Let sit for 15 minutes. Gently scrub with a brush. Hose down or wipe clean.

164. Remove Stains on Driveways. Spray the concrete thoroughly. Let sit for 15 minutes. Gently scrub with a brush. Hose down or wipe clean.

165. Remove Stains on Home Siding. Spray the siding thoroughly. Let sit for 15 minutes. Gently scrub with a brush. Hose down or wipe clean.

166. Remove Stains on Brick. Spray the brick thoroughly. Let sit for 15 minutes. Gently scrub with a brush. Hose down or wipe clean.

167. Wallpaper Removal. Spray wallpaper area with 1 capful of Thieves Household Cleaner mixed with 1 quart of water. Allow it to soak in for 10 minutes. Gently pull the paper from the bottom edge upward. Spray and wipe the wall area underneath once the paper is removed.

168. Mist Live Plants. Mist plants with 1 capful of Thieves Household Cleaner per quart of water.

169. Sanitize Sponges. Soak overnight in 2 capfuls of Thieves Household cleaner in one quart of water.

170. Sanitize Rags. Soak overnight in 2 capfuls of Thieves Household cleaner in one quart of water.

171. Sanitize Toothbrush(es). Soak overnight in 1 capful of Thieves Household cleaner in one 8-ounce glass of water. Add 3 drops of Thieves Essential Oil. Rinse thoroughly.

172. Paint stains. Massage Thieves Household Cleaner in full strength on the stain to loosen and liquefy. Repeat. Hand wash or launder directly afterward.

173. Vegetable/Fruit Staining on Appliances. Soak metal blades, plastic internal parts, and lids for 30 minutes in a mixture of Thieves Household Cleaner (full-strength) and 4 Young Living Detoxzyme® capsules. Scrub gently with a nylon scrub brush.

174. Clean Sneakers. Soak a rag in a solution of 1 capful of Thieves Household Cleaner per quart of water and gently clean all of the light parts of shoes.

175. Shoe Odor. Using a solution of 1 capful of Thieves Household Cleaner per quart of water, mist the insides of shoes between each wearing to keep fresh.

176. Deodorize/Disinfect Diaper Pail. Pour ½ capful of Thieves Household Cleaner in the bottom of the pail. Rotate the pail so that the solution covers every surface. Allow to sit for an hour. Wipe clean.

177. Deodorize Carpets. Combine 1 capful of Thieves Household Cleaner with one 8-ounce box of pure baking soda in a glass jar. Mix thoroughly. Sprinkle over carpets. Allow to sit for 15 minutes. Vacuum thoroughly.

178. Deodorize Vacuum Cleaner. Combine 1 capful of Thieves Household Cleaner with one 8-ounce box of pure baking soda in a glass jar. Add a tablespoon to the vacuum bag or bag-less receptacle.

179. Clean Produce. Use 1 capful of Thieves Household Cleaner in 24 ounces of water (3 cups) to make your own Fruit & Veggie spray that cleans off pesticides, residues, and germs.

180. Protect Pets. Gently mist your pet's fur coat with a solution of 1 capful of Thieves Household Cleaner per quart of water.

181. Replace Automotive Degreaser. Use Thieves Household Cleaner in full concentration as a replacement for chemical-filled petroleum-based automotive degreaser products.

182. Replace Paint Degreaser. Use Thieves Household Cleaner in full concentration as a replacement for chemical-filled petroleum-based automotive degreaser products.

183. Clean Garbage Cans/Pails. Pour 3 capfuls of Thieves Household Cleaner in the bottom of the can/pail. Rotate the can/pail so that the solution covers every surface. Allow to sit overnight. Add 3 gallons of water. Using toilet scrubbing brush, clean every surface. Turn can/pail on its side. Hose down until clean.

184. Clean Pet Bowls. In a solution of 1 capful per quart, clean your pets' bowls. Rinse thoroughly.

185. Economically Replace Cleaners 1. Replace 128 all-purpose cleaning bottles (at 25-30 ounces each) for 88 cents a bottle by purchasing a 64-ounce bottle of Thieves Household Cleaner.

186. Economically Replace Cleaners 2. Replace 128 all-purpose cleaning bottles (at 25-30 ounces each) for 67 cents a bottle by purchasing a 64-ounce bottle of Thieves Household Cleaner and becoming a member of Young Living to enjoy wholesale pricing.

187. Economically Replace Cleaners 3. Replace 128 all-purpose cleaning bottles (at 25-30 ounces each) for 51 cents a bottle by purchasing a 64-ounce bottle of Thieves Household Cleaner and becoming a member of Young Living to enjoy wholesale pricing AND join Essential Rewards for up to 25% back in rewards after 12 months.

188. Make a Wood Surface Cleaner. Mix 1 capful of Thieves Household Cleaner with 1 cup of olive oil. Use it to wipe down wooden furniture, cabinets, and fixtures (such as banisters, mantles, or handrails).

189. Polish Wooden Frames. Mix 1 capful of Thieves Household Cleaner with 1 cup of olive oil. Use it to polish picture frames, mirror frames, or other items you dust.

190. Polish Stone Items. Mix 1 capful of Thieves Household Cleaner with 1 cup of olive oil. Use it to polish stone fixtures, marble/travertine tiles, and coasters.

191. Wash the Car. Mix 1 capful of Thieves Household Cleaner with 1 cup of olive oil. Use it to wipe down wooden furniture, cabinets, and fixtures (such as banisters, mantles, or handrails).

192. Add Power to a Power Washer. Mix 1-2 capfuls in your power washer reservoir to boost cleaning power for every power washer task.

193. Clean Aquariums. After moving your fish out of the tank, use 1 capful of Thieves Household Cleaner per quart of water to clean and descale the aquarium. Rinse thoroughly before refilling the tank and returning the fish.

THIEVES® LAUNDRY SOAP

194. High Efficiency Washers: Add 1/4 cap of Thieves Laundry Soap depending on the size of the load and level of soil.

195. Conventional Washers: Add 1/2 cap of Thieves Laundry Soap depending on the size of the load and level of soil.

196. Replace Delicate Detergent. Use 1 tablespoon of Thieves Laundry Soap in the sink to hand wash delicates.

197. Replace Stain Pre-treatment. Use Thieves Laundry Soap in full concentration with an eye dropper to pre-treat stains.

198. Replace Fabric Freshener Sprays. Use Thieves Laundry Soap in a mixture of 1 tablespoon per 16 ounces of water to gently mist dry clothes before fluffing in the dryer.

199. Wrinkle Releaser/Freshener. Use Thieves Laundry Soap in a mixture of 1 tablespoon per 16 ounces of water to gently mist clothes and help pull the wrinkles out. Fluff in dryer.

200. De-Gum Adhesive. Apply directly to the gummy adhesive on price labels/ stickers.

THIEVES® SPRAY

201. Doorknobs. Spray on doorknobs in public restrooms to kill germs.

202. Hands. Spray hands before and after shaking hands with a lot of people.

203. Pens. Spray pens, pencils, and scissors periodically to help sanitize.

204. Dog Leash. Spray on the dog leash after each walk to help sanitize.

205. Airplane Restrooms. Spray in restrooms on airplanes to help sanitize.

206. Public Restrooms. Spray in public restrooms to help sanitize.

207. Produce. Spray on fruits and vegetables and fruits when washing them. Rinse thoroughly.

208. Foreign Countries. Carry for protection in countries with risk of germ exposure.

209. Freshen Air. Use as an air freshener for cooking odors or other unwanted smells.

210. Gym Equipment. Spray all the equipment you use at the gym instead of the provided chemical-laden spray.

211. Carts. Use to disinfect shopping cart handles at the supermarket or large retail store.

212. Classroom. Use in the classroom for desks, tables and other items.

213. Discourage Mold. Spray on shower stalls and bathroom walls to help reduce mold.

214. Handles. Spray on handles & parts of doors in your home to kill germs.

215. Public Toilet Seats. Spray on public toilet seat when there is no seat cover.

216. Toilet Paper. Spray on toilet paper to help you "wipe clean."

217. Toilet Handle. Spray on toilet handle to kill germs before flushing.

218. Sanitize Shoes 1. Spray on the bottoms of your shoes before bringing them in your house. Allow to dry before putting them away.

219. Sanitize Shoes 2. Spray on the bottoms of shoes, laces, and insides between wearings.

220. Clean/Sanitize Luggage 1. Spray the cloth on your empty suitcase to clean the inside & outside.

221. Clean/Sanitize Luggage 2. Spray the handles of your luggage to clean.

222. Clean/Sanitize Gym Bag. Spray your gym bag inside and outside between washings to disinfect.

223. Touchscreens. Spray a touchscreen (when the device is off) to kill germs.

224. Bedding. When a child is sick, spray the bedding before and after they sleep. (Change it often.)

225. Stuffed Animals. Spray your child's stuffed animals. Put them in the dryer to help kill germs.

226. Games & Media. Spray your DVD cases, CD cases, game cases, game console, and other media to help kill germs.

227. Toys. Spray your child's toys between uses to help kill germs

228. Car Upholstery. Spray your car upholstery to help reduce germs & mold.

229. Car Handles & Dash. Spray your car handles/dashboard. Wipe clean with a soft rag.

230. Window Bases. Spray windows where kids and pets touch with hands, paws, & noses.

231. Countertops. Spray down countertops after cleaning to help disinfect.

232. Camping Dishes. When camping, spray & wipe dishes after cleaning or instead of water cleaning.

233. Camping Tables/Benches. When camping, spray and wipe down tables and benches before use.

234. Sick Room. In room where someone has been coughing and sneezing, lightly mist the drapes, carpets, & surface bedding.

235. HVAC 1. Remove HVAC vent covers. Spray & wipe clean. Spray the interior duct & wipe down. Replace vent covers.

236. HVAC 2. Spray the cold-air return vent & wipe clean.

237. HVAC 3. Spray the HVAC filter to reduce mold, mildew, & germs.

238. Travel 1. Wipe down your cabin on a cruise.

239. All-Purpose for Bathroom Sink. Using the all-purpose cleaner spray recipe above and soft, lint-free rag, spray and wipe away germs, scum, mineral, and stains from the bathroom sink.

240. All-Purpose for Toilet Bowl. Using the all-purpose cleaner spray recipe above, spray the inside of the bowl. Wait 2 minutes. Spray again. Use a toilet bowl brush to scrub away stains. Flush. Repeat.

241. Bathroom Floor 1. Spray the bathroom floor. With a clean towel, wipe gently.

242. Bathroom Floor 2. Spray the bathroom floor. Mop dry with clean, soft mop.

243. Baseboards. Spray the baseboards. Wipe gently clean.

244. Shower. Spray the inside of the shower. Wait 2 minutes. Spray again. Pay close attention to stained, soap-scum-ridden areas, or moldy spots. Rinse clean.

245. Bathtub. Spray the inside of the bathtub thoroughly. Wait 2 minutes. Spray again. Pay close attention to stained, soap-scum-ridden areas, or moldy spots. Rinse clean.

246. Kitchen Sink. Spray the inside of the kitchen sink. Wait 2 minutes. Spray again. Pay close attention to stained, soap-scum-ridden areas, or moldy spots. Rinse clean.

247. Counter Tops. Spray the countertops as normal. Wipe clean and dry with a soft rag.

248. Stovetops. Spray the stovetop as normal. Wipe clean and dry with a soft rag.

249. Floors 1. Spray the floors, and wipe clean and dry with a soft rag.

250. Floors 2. Spray a soft, clean towel with the solution. Walk gently across the floors to clean up dust and give the floors a marvelous shine.

251. Chrome Fixtures. Spray the fixtures, and wipe clean and dry with a soft, lint-free rag.

252. Doors. Spray the areas of doors where greasy hands tend to touch and leave marks. Pay close attention to where feet also scuff bottoms. Wipe clean with a soft cloth.

253. Cleaning Tools. Spray sponges, rags, and mop heads, and handles to clean and disinfect.

254. Clothes Freshening. Spray to freshen clothes and kill germs.

255. Purifier for Clothes. Spray to areas of clothes that come in contact with potentially dirty seats, germs, etc.

256. Room Clarifier Spray. Spray room to clarify the air.

257. Bathroom Freshening. Spray to freshen the bathroom after use.

258. Toilet Freshening. Spray the bowl 5x before each use to freshen the toilet.

259. Kitchen. Spray to freshen the kitchen after cooking.

260. House Freshening. Spray to freshen the whole house and cleanse the air.

261. Purify Pet Cages. Spray and wipe down pet cages to create a healthy environment.

262. Purify Pet Beds. Gently mist pet beds to create a healthy environment, deodorize, and prevent pests.

THIEVES® WIPES

Aromatic · Cleansing

263. Doorknobs. Use Thieves Wipes to wipe doorknobs and other things touched by the public.

264. Piano. Use Thieves Wipes to wipe public piano keys to clean and disinfect them.

265. Kids' Hands. Use Thieves Wipes to clean children's hands when traveling.

266. Rest Areas. Use Thieves Wipes to clean hands at rest areas when soap & water are limited.

267. Steering Wheel. Use Thieves Wipes on the steering wheel of every vehicle.

268. Gearshift. Use Thieves Wipes on the gearshift of each vehicle you drive.

269. Console. Use Thieves Wipes on the console of every vehicle.

270. Car Handles. Use Thieves Wipes on the car handles of every vehicle.

271. Bicycle Handles. Use Thieves Wipes on the handles of kids' bikes.

272. Public Telephones. Use Thieves Wipes on public telephones to help sanitize before and after use.

273. Public Keyboards. Use Thieves Wipes on public computer keyboards.

274. Public Computer Mice. Use Thieves Wipes on public touchscreens.

275. Public Touchscreens. Use Thieves Wipes on public computer mouse devices.

276. Airplane Seat. Use Thieves Wipes on airplane seat.

277. Airplane Headrest. Use Thieves Wipes on airplane headrest.

278. Airplane Buttons. Use Thieves Wipes on airplane buttons.

279. Airplane Armrests. Use Thieves Wipes on airplane armrests.

280. Airplane Trays. Use Thieves Wipes on airplane trays.

281. Airplane Bathrooms. Use Thieves Wipes on airplane bathrooms.

282. Bus Seats. Use Thieves Wipes on bus seats.

283. Bus Headrests. Use Thieves Wipes on bus headrests.

284. Theater Seats. Use Thieves Wipes on theater seats.

285. Theater Headrests. Use Thieves Wipes on theater headrests.

286. Theater Buttons. Use Thieves Wipes on theater buttons.

287. Theater Trays. Use Thieves Wipes on theater trays.

288. Shopping Carts. Use Thieves Wipes on shopping carts.

289. Park Benches. Use Thieves Wipes on park benches.

290. Cabs/Ubers. Use Thieves Wipes (respectfully) in cabs or Uber cars.

291. Pets 1. Use Thieves Wipes to freshen your dog or cat.

292. Pets 2. Use Thieves Wipes on pets' paws after they come in from outside.

293. Pets 2. Use Thieves Wipes to wipe for pets after they "do their business."

THIEVES® HOUSEHOLD CLEANER SINGLE-USE PACKETS

294. Make an All-Purpose Cleaner. Mix 1 tablespoon of Thieves Household Cleaner (from the Single-Use Packets) with 2-3 cups of distilled water. Store in 2-3 8-ounce amber glass spray bottles.

295. Make a Heavy Degreaser. Combine 1 tablespoon Thieves Household Cleaner (from the Single-Use Packets) with 1 cup of distilled water.

296. Make a Carpet/Upholstery Spot Cleaner. Mix 1 tablespoon of Thieves Household Cleaner (from the Single-Use Packets) with 6 cups of water. Combine thoroughly.

297. Make a Deep Cleaning Scrub. Mix equal parts Thieves Household Cleaner (from the Single-Use Packets) and baking soda to form a thick paste.

298. Replace Automotive Degreaser. Use Thieves Household Cleaner (from the Single-Use Packets) in full concentration as a replacement for chemical-filled petroleum-based automotive degreaser products.

299. Replace Paint Degreaser. Use Thieves Household Cleaner (from the Single-Use Packets) in full concentration as a replacement for chemical-filled petroleum-based automotive degreaser products.

300. Make a Wood Surface Cleaner. Mix 1 tablespoon of Thieves Household Cleaner (from the Single-Use Packets) with 1 cup of olive oil. Use it to wipe down wooden furniture, cabinets, and fixtures (such as banisters, mantles, or handrails).

THIEVES® AROMABRIGHT™ TOOTHPASTE

Aromatic · Cleansing

301. Replace Your Toothpaste. Clean your teeth as usual using Thieves AromaBright Toothpaste to prevent cavities.

302. Support Healing Teeth. Clean your teeth as usual using Thieves AromaBright Toothpaste when teeth have been damaged or chipped to protect them and support healing.

303. Support Healthy Gums. Brush as usual using Thieves AromaBright Toothpaste to prevent gum disease and support healthy gums.

304. Freshen Breath. Use as directed to brush away odor-causing bacteria and freshen breath.

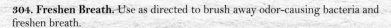

305. Underarm Deodorant. Apply as an alternative to underarm deodorant.

306. Stick Away. Apply to hands to remove stubborn, sticky substances.

307. Produce Wash. Use to wash fruits and vegetables from supermarket.

308. Tile Grout Scrub. Use as a scrub for tile or grout.

THIEVES® DENTAROMA ULTRA™ TOOTHPASTE

309. Replace Your Toothpaste. Clean your teeth as usual using Thieves Dentarome Ultra Toothpaste to prevent cavities.

310. Support Healing Teeth. Use when teeth have been damaged or chipped to protect them and support healing.

311. Support Healthy Gums. Use to prevent gum disease and support healthy gums.

312. Freshen Breath. Use as directed to brush away odor-causing bacteria and freshen breath.

313. Fix Cloudy Car Headlights. Add a dollop of toothpaste to a clean, soft sponge. Rub car headlights gently for several minutes. Rinse away.

314. Underarm Deodorant. Apply as an alternative to underarm deodorant.

315. Stick Away. Apply to hands to remove stubborn, sticky substances.

316. Produce Wash. Use to wash fruits and vegetables from supermarket.

317. Tile Grout Scrub. Use as a scrub for tile or grout.

THIEVES® DENTAROME PLUS™ TOOTHPASTE

Aromatic · Cleansing

318. Replace Your Toothpaste. Clean your teeth as usual using Thieves Dentarome Plus Toothpaste to prevent cavities.

319. Support Healing Teeth. Use when teeth have been damaged or chipped to protect them and support healing.

320. Support Healthy Gums. Use to prevent gum disease and support healthy gums.

321. Freshen Breath. Use as directed to brush away odor-causing bacteria and freshen breath.

322. Replace Your Pet's Toothpaste. Clean your pet's teeth using the same amount suggested for your regular toothpaste or the same amount you would use for a small child.

323. Fix Cloudy Car Headlights. Add a dollop of toothpaste to a clean, soft sponge. Rub car headlights gently for several minutes. Rinse away.

324. Underarm Deodorant. Apply as an alternative to underarm deodorant.

325. Stick Away. Apply to hands to remove stubborn, sticky substances.

326. Produce Wash. Use to wash fruits and vegetables from supermarket.

327. Tile Grout Scrub. Use as a scrub for tile or grout.

THIEVES® DENTAL FLOSS

Aromatic · Cleansing

328. Replace Your Current Floss. Floss your teeth as you ordinarily would, using Thieves Dental Floss.

THIEVES® FRESH ESSENCE PLUS™ MOUTHWASH

329. Support Healing Teeth. Use when teeth have been damaged or chipped to protect them and support healing.

330. Support Healthy Gums. Use to prevent gum disease and support healthy gums.

331. Freshen Breath. Use as directed to gargle away odor-causing bacteria and freshen breath.

332. Sing Clearly. Gargle before a singing engagement to clear mucus.

333. Alternative Hand Sanitizer. Use as a waterless hand sanitizer.

334. Hand Smoothing. Rub on hands to make them soft, fresh and smooth.

335. Acne. Using a cotton swab, apply to face as a toner/astringent to help clear acne.

336. DIY Breath Spray. Transfer to a 1-ounce amber glass sprayer bottle. Spray in your mouth to freshen breath on the go.

337. Throat Protection. Transfer to a 1-ounce amber glass sprayer bottle. Spray your mouth and throat to help prevent germs.

338. Healthy Dog/Cat Teeth. Apply with a cotton swab to where the teeth meet the gum line on your dog or cat to support oral health.

THIEVES® CLEANSING SOAP

Aromatic · Cleansing

339. Laundry Pre-Wash. Dampen the Thieves Cleansing Soap bar. Rub gently on stains as a pre-wash stain remover.

340. Deodorant Soap. Use as a deodorant soap when showering.

341. Wash Away Germs. Use as a bar hand soap to reduce germs.

342. Clean Under Nails. Scratch fingernails across a dry bar soap to clean under fingernails. Soak fingers in warm water for 1 minute. Using an orange stick, gently scrape the soap, dirt, and germs away. Rinse.

THIEVES® FOAMING HAND SOAP

Aromatic · Cleansing

343. Hand Cleaning. Wash hands thoroughly with Thieves Foaming Hand Soap and warm water.

344. Laundry Pre-Treat. Use two pumps of Thieves Foaming Hand Soap on a stain. Massage into the stain gently. Launder according to clothing tag directions. (Avoid use on dry-clean only items.)

345. DIY Cleaning Wipes. Use 2 pumps of Thieves Foaming Hand Soap on a sturdy paper towel. "Fold" the foam into the paper towel and use as you would a cleaning wipe.

THIEVES® WATERLESS HAND PURIFIER

Aromatic · Cleansing

346. Sanitize Hands. Use as directed to sanitize hands.

347. Sanitizing Wipes. Use with a sturdy paper towel to create a sanitizing wipe.

348. Clean Ink. Apply to an ink stain. Massage gently into the stain. Use a paper towel to dab out the ink.

THIEVES® COUGH DROPS

Aromatic · Cleansing

349. Stave Off the Ick. Put in your mouth at the first sign of a sniffle or scratchy throat.

350. Sing Your Best. Take right before singing performances to support a clear singing voice.

351. Help the Healing. Use while recovering from a cold.

352. Help During Allergy Season. Use during allergy season to prevent a scratchy throat.

353. Share With the Choir. Keep a box for choir practice and share with everyone before singing.

354. Airplane Defense. Have one in your mouth before boarding and airplane and throughout the flight to support your healthy immune system.

355. Speak Smoothly. Use before a speaking engagement.

356. Event Talk. Use before going to events with large crowds—conventions, meetings, parties, funerals, or weddings—to keep your throat clear and your breath fresh.

THIEVES® HARD LOZENGES

Aromatic · Cleansing

357. Stave Off the Ick. Put in your mouth at the first sign of a sniffle or scratchy throat.

358. Sing Your Best. Take right before singing performances to support a clear singing voice.

359. Help the Healing. Use while recovering from a cold.

360. Help During Allergy Season. Use during allergy season to prevent a scratchy throat.

361. Share With the Choir. Keep a box for choir practice and share with everyone before singing.

362. Airplane Defense. Have one in your mouth before boarding and airplane and throughout the flight to support your healthy immune system.

363. Speak Smoothly. Use before a speaking engagement.

364. Event Talk. Use before going to events with large crowds—conventions, meetings, parties, funerals, or weddings—to keep your throat clear and your breath fresh.